Disney in Details

A Scavenger Hunt Through the *Walt Disney World* Resort

By **Jen Darcy** and **Jennifer Eastwood**

Disney

EDITIONS

New York

LOOK AROUND YOU

The *Walt Disney World* Resort is rich with details—each one layered on top of the next to form a beautifully intricate backdrop. These details are what allow Guests to so easily become swept away in the story of the Parks, transporting them to another time and place.

For newcomers, the details swirl around in the background like a brightly colored kaleidoscope and lay the foundation for that magical feeling Guests experience during a visit. For seasoned veterans, the details are like well-acquainted friends who offer greetings on each return visit. Some seem constant and help maintain a Guest's sense of familiarity; others change through the years and stimulate that curiosity of what new wonders await in this constantly evolving place. But regardless of whether it's a first or fiftieth trip, the details become forever connected to Guests' cherished family memories.

This guide to the *Walt Disney World* Resort serves as a companion to those details. With each page, see how many you can place as you venture around the highlights of the World. Are you someone who knows every nook and cranny here better than you know your own backyard? Do color schemes and patterns live in the back of your mind? Or, are you simply up for gaining an appreciation of all the imagination come-to-life that's put into this special Vacation Kingdom? To all who come on this happy journey, welcome.

—Jen Darcy and Jennifer Eastwood

Where in the World?

b

a

c

Think you know where to find these Disney details? Check the inside cover to see if you're right!

3

Main Street, U.S.A. Area

The Main Street, U.S.A. Area brings harmony to a *Magic Kingdom* Park visit. This idealized turn-of-the-century town sets the upbeat tone and organizational simplicity for a Guest's overall experience. Inside this area, shops like the Main Street Confectionery provide a whimsical world full of delicious scents. Show-tune orchestrations resound along the street—as do the tunes played by the pianist outside Casey's Corner. At the end of the street stands Cinderella Castle, a gateway to a fanciful wonderland.

PARK

JACK OLSEN

SILHOUETTES

Where in the World?

a

b

Think you know where to find these Disney details? Check the inside cover to see if you're right!

5

THE MAGIC KINGDOM
WALT DISNEY WORLD

6

Walt Disney World Railroad
Four impressive locomotives—named Walter E. Disney, Roy O. Disney, Lilly Belle, and Roger E. Broggie—chug along the outer edges of *Magic Kingdom* Park daily and offer a relaxing ride.

From Town Square to the Hub

Street vendors carry colorful Mickey-shaped balloons, while the Dapper Dans serenade passersby during impromptu a cappella concerts. Belgian horses with trolleys in tow invite Guests for a loop along the street. At night, tiny white bulbs illuminate the rooftops, and firefly-like lights twinkle in the small trees encircling Blaine Gibson's bronze sculptures of classic characters and Walt Disney himself.

Where in the World?

Think you know where to find these Disney details? Check the inside cover to see if you're right!

a

b

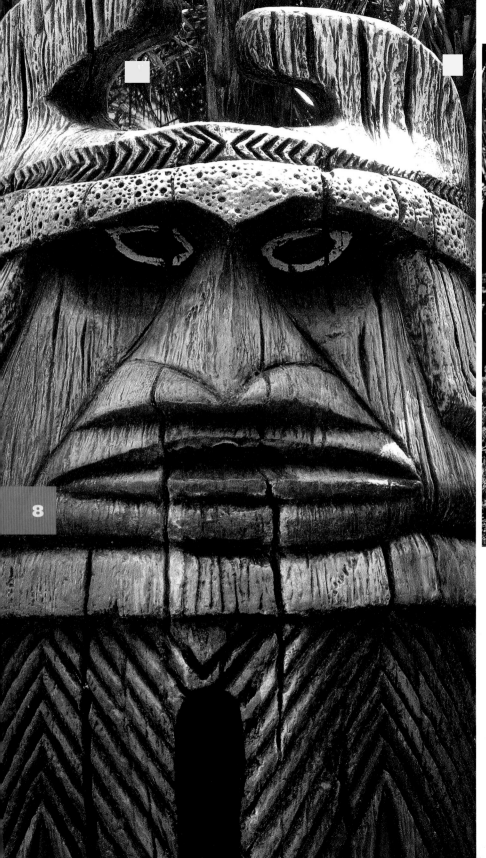

Adventureland Area

Inspired by Disney's Academy Award-winning nature series, True-Life Adventures (1948–1960), this land builds on the excitement that comes from not quite knowing what's around the next bend. Firelit torches line the walkways, their flames dancing in a gentle breeze at dusk. In the light of day, jewels embedded in the sidewalks around the Arabian marketplace sparkle in the sun. Bring a keen eye and a curious spirit to discover all the treasures hidden here.

Swiss Family Treehouse Attraction

A sixty-foot-tall banyan tree might look natural in central Florida, but this one serves up an open-house tour unlike any other. Based on the 1960 Disney film *Swiss Family Robinson*, this multilevel tree house invites Guests to climb pathways up and under all sorts of twisted branches.

Where in the World?

Think you know where to find these Disney details? Check the inside cover to see if you're right!

a

b

9

Jungle Cruise Attraction

Travel down exotic jungle rivers with a wise, wisecracking skipper. From an elephant bathing pool to a deserted temple crawling with cobras, adventure awaits around every river bend. Guests face charging hippos, headhunters, and hungry tigers—armed solely with the captain's vast arsenal of puns.

Where in the World?

a **b**

Think you know where to find these Disney details? Check the inside cover to see if you're right!

THE ENCHANTED

ENCHANTED TIKI ROOM

UNDER NEW MANAGEMENT!

11

Walt Disney's Enchanted Tiki Room Attraction

Tweet this: the tiki room's original hosts—Jose, Fritz, Pierre, and Michael—are back and better than ever, ushering in a new era for this Polynesian musical revue. The four avian emcees introduce a vibrant show that harkens back to the classic *Disneyland* Park attraction. Even Guests take part in the fun, raising their voices along with the parrots and tikis as they perform "Let's All Sing Like the Birdies Sing."

The Magic Carpets of Aladdin Attraction

Want a taste of Agrabah in the middle of the Adventureland Area? Your wish is granted! Fly high, low, or in a zany wavy pattern on one of the sixteen carpets circling Genie's lamp. Just watch out for the camels; they spit.

Where **a** in the **World?**

Think you know where to find these Disney details? Check the inside cover to see if you're right!

b

Pirates of the Caribbean Attraction

Avast, ye land lovers, there be rough waters ahead. Through a ghostly cavern, past shipwrecked skeletons, and down a waterfall, Guests encounter Captain Barbossa on the hunt for the notorious Captain Jack Sparrow, as bands of singing scalawags plunder a treasure-filled Caribbean town.

Splash Mountain Attraction

Br'er Fox is searching for something other than a good Laughin' Place: Br'er Rabbit. Log boats carry Guests past characters inspired by the 1946 film *Song of the South* and head for a fifty-two-and-a-half-foot plummet into a briar patch.

Frontierland Area

Yee-haw! Based on U.S. pioneer history from 1790 to 1880, the Frontierland Area abounds with opportunities. The warm color pallet soaks in the sun, while the smell of smoked turkey legs wafts through the air. Foot-stomping melodies ramble through a tumbleweed town; simple and slow banjo tunes float along the riverside walkways. After traveling far and wide, this land serves as a welcomed outpost for the brave at heart.

Where in the **World?**

a

Think you know where to find these Disney details? Check the inside cover to see if you're right!

b

15

Walt Disney World Railroad Station
With the addition of the Splash Mountain Attraction in 1992, the Frontierland Area needed a new, elevated train station—*bearing* the old-world charm of the 1800s.

Big Thunder Mountain Attraction

The sound of train tracks cracking under the locomotive's weight echoes through the cave. Rocks teeter on the brink of tumbling over head. Then *whoosh*—Guests rush by abandoned tunnels, iridescent cavern springs, and a flooded mine town on "the wildest ride in the wilderness."

Tom Sawyer Island Attraction

Drift on the great Rivers of America aboard a log raft. Once docked, Guests explore a secluded island that conceals many mysterious hideaways that are inspired by Mark Twain's classic novels.

Country Bear Jamboree Show

Big Al may live up to his name, but his stage power is way bigger—as is the paw-tappin' presence of master of ceremonies Henry, superstar-swinger Teddi Barra, and all the other critters a strummin' and a singin' daily at Grizzly Hall.

Where in the World?

Think you know where to find these Disney details? Check the inside cover to see if you're right!

a

b

Liberty Square Area

The Liberty Square Area exudes respect for the cornerstone ideals that are the bedrock of the United States of America: life, liberty, and the pursuit of happiness. Cobblestone pathways wind underfoot, while sounds of fife and drum stream through the air. But among the colonial American icons, such as replicas of the Liberty Bell and Liberty Tree, it might be the public stockades that best hint at the macabre experience awaiting Guests at the Hudson River Valley-inspired mansion just down the path.

Think you know where to find these Disney details? Check the inside cover to see if you're right!

Where in the World?

a

b

HARPER'S MILL

Haunted Mansion Attraction

Perched atop a hillside, an elegant-looking Gothic manor welcomes foolish mortals to the Haunted Mansion Attraction. Guests board "Doom Buggies" for a guided tour of the estate that's swinging with happy haunts, chilling special effects, and a ghoulishly delightful theme song.

19

Hall of Presidents Attraction

Dressed in historically accurate hand-tailored clothing, *Audio-Animatronics* Figures of the nation's presidents come together during this twenty-five-minute tribute to American history and the U.S. presidency.

Where in the **World?**

a

Think you know where to find these Disney details? Check the inside cover to see if you're right!

b

21

Liberty Belle Riverboat

A welcomed sight from the banks of both the Frontierland Area and the Liberty Square Area, this 450-passenger paddle wheeler runs on steam. Narrated by Mark Twain, the cruise presents a perspective from beyond the landlubbers' paths.

Fantasyland Area

Forever adorned in medieval-tournament banners, flags, and other displays of pageantry, the Fantasyland Area fosters a sense of never-ending enchantment. Equally as inspiring is the promise of an entirely new expansion scheduled to open in phases, beginning in late 2012 with an attraction themed to *The Little Mermaid* (1989) and areas dedicated to *Beauty and the Beast* (1991) and *Snow White and the Seven Dwarfs* (1937).

22

"it's a small world" Attraction

Based on designs by Imagineer Mary Blair, this buoyant boat ride celebrates people's differences and similarities around the world. Colorfully costumed dolls sing (and yodel!) the classic theme song.

Peter Pan's Flight Attraction

Boarding a flying pirate ship, Guests follow the boy who never grows up and the three Darling children out the nursery window, over aerial views of London, and on to Never Land. Just keep a sharp eye out for the sinister Captain Hook.

Disney's **FastPass** Distribution

RETURN BETWEEN 12:30 AND 1:00

Where in the World?

Think you know where to find these Disney details? Check the inside cover to see if you're right!

a

b

Cinderella Castle

Rising 189 feet in the air, the castle is the quintessential icon of the *Walt Disney World* Resort. Upstairs at Cinderella's Royal Table, Guests dine in style under medieval columns and stained glass windows. In the main archway tunnel below, more than a thousand brilliantly colored tiles form a mosaic that retells the rags-to-riches story of our heroine and flanks the entrance to the Bibbidi Bobbidi Boutique beauty salon, where young Guests can transform into princesses with the wave of some clips, combs, and curlers.

Prince Charming Regal Carrousel

Built by the Philadelphia Toboggan Co. in 1917 for the Detroit Palace Garden Park and later moved to the Maplewood Olympic Park in New Jersey, where Imagineers found it, the carrousel is now renovated and themed to the 1950 animated film.

Where in the World?

a

Think you know where to find these Disney details? Check the inside cover to see if you're right!

25

b

Mickey's PhilharMagic Attraction

Mickey's hat from *Fantasia*'s "The Sorcerer's Apprentice" (1940) sequence rouses new magical mayhem—this time in 3-D on a 150-foot-wide screen.

Snow White's Scary Adventures Attraction

Having showcased the first full-length animated film, *Snow White and the Seven Dwarfs* (1937), since *Magic Kingdom* Park opened in 1971, this black-light dark ride has weaved Guests past frightening forests and the wicked Queen herself. With the *Fantasyland* Area expansion, The Seven Dwarfs Mine Attraction—a first-of-its-kind swinging coaster—will transport Guests on a musical journey into the heart of the diamond mines.

Where in the **World?**

a
b

Think you know where to find these Disney details? Check the inside cover to see if you're right!

Dumbo the Flying Elephant Attraction

Like a proud ringmaster, Timothy Mouse stands atop a red and white balloon, watching out for those sixteen elephants whirling over the Fantasyland Area. As part of the expansion, the attraction will double in size and move to new circus grounds (in the redesigned space of the Mickey's Toontown Fair Area).

The Many Adventures of Winnie the Pooh Attraction

Have a rumbly in your tumbly? Time for something sweet! And nothing's sweeter than Winnie the Pooh and his Hundred-Acre Wood chums. On board a honey-pot car, Guests bounce with Tigger, feel the blustery wind at Rabbit's, escape heffalumps and woozles with Pooh, float past Piglet's, and wish Eeyore many happy returns.

where in the **World?**

a

b

Think you know where to find these Disney details? Check the inside cover to see if you're right!

29

Mad Tea Party Attraction
Much like the Mad Hatter's pocket watch, this two-minute teacup twirl is exactly right twice a day. In the daylight, tea party topiaries intrigue curious eyes, but after dark, glowing paper lanterns add even more whimsy to perhaps the most playful scene from *Alice in Wonderland* (1951).

Tomorrowland Area

Reminiscent of science fiction stories of the 1920s and 1930s, this intergalactic metropolis is home to talking robots and aliens. Jagged red rocks interweave with rocket-ship towers and space-age gadgets. At night, a blaze of neon light pulsates in all shades of the rainbow—proving the Tomorrowland Area to be one cool corner of the cosmos.

Tomorrowland Indy Speedway Attraction

Push the pedal to the metal along a more than 2,000-foot-long course, touring the outer edges of both the Fantasyland Area and the Tomorrowland Area's hub.

Astro Orbiter Attraction

High atop Rocket Tower Plaza, planets, moons, and asteroids whirl around Guests spinning in one of twelve star jets. Satellites with flashing lights add to the exhilaration of this two-minute lunar loop.

a

Where in the World?

Think you know where to find these Disney details? Check the inside cover to see if you're right!

b

KERITS

Space Mountain Attraction

To *astro* or *astronaut*; that is the question. This roller coaster-like thrill ride rushes Guests into outer space at speeds of up to twenty-eight miles per hour. With the 2009 renovation, Imagineers sealed up any outdoor-light intrusions, thus allowing the stars in the indoor intergalactic sky to shine brighter than ever before.

Tomorrowland Transit Authority PeopleMover

This highway of the future transports Guests in comfy blue cars motored by electromagnets on the track. The relaxing ride presents a bird's-eye view of the Tomorrowland Area, including the inside of the Space Mountain Attraction.

Carousel of Progress Attraction

Originally constructed for the 1964–1965 New York World's Fair, the twenty-one-minute stage show presents one American family's experiences with evolving technology. The show features four segmented decades—all as the theater cleverly revolves around the central stage.

a

Where in the World?

Think you know where to find these Disney details? Check the inside cover to see if you're right!

b

Walt Disney's

CAROUSEL OF PROGRESS

Buzz Lightyear's Space Ranger Spin Attraction

Board an XP-37 pod—equipped with laser-gun action, full-spinning capability, and a score-keeping display—to zap stolen batteries across the universe and help Buzz Lightyear restore interplanetary peace.

Monsters, Inc. Laugh Floor Attraction

Even if you're not with *that guy*, the Living Characters in this Monstropolis comedy show will find a way to tickle your funny bone. Monster of Ceremonies Mike Wazowski, along with comedians like Buddy Boil, spontaneously joke around with audiences daily.

MONSTERS of COMEDY

Stitch's GREAT ESCAPE!

Where in the World?

ⓐ

Think you know where to find these Disney details? Check the inside cover to see if you're right!

ⓑ

35

Stitch's Great Escape! Attraction

Stitch is one of the universe's most-wanted convicts. After breaking out during a prison-containment demonstration, the little blue alien (and his chili dog breath!) pays an up-close-and-personal visit to each Guest in the audience.

NIGHTTIME MAGIC

SpectroMagic Parade
More than six-hundred-thousand tiny lights and hundreds of fiber-optic strands dance on floats themed to *Sleeping Beauty*, *Fantasia*, *The Little Mermaid*, and more. (Note: The magic returns after the Main Street Electrical Parade revival ends its run.)

Main Street Electrical Parade
Along with thousands of sparkling lights, the electrosynthomagnetic sounds of the infamous "Baroque Hoedown" mix with classic Disney songs. Pete, who perches atop his imaginary dragon Elliott, is joined by Tinker Bell, Pinocchio, Snow White, and many others in a spectactular display of splendor.

AND IMAGINATION

Wishes Nighttime Spectacular
Whether seen from inside the *Magic Kingdom* Park or from afar, the spirit surrounding this fireworks festival energizes Guests with hope and wonder.

Where in the World?

Think you know where to find these Disney details? Check the inside cover to see if you're right!

a

b

EPCOT®

Future World Area
Nowhere in *Epcot®* offers better exploration opportunities than the Future World Area. All five senses are tested and delighted by innovative techniques across varied areas of study. Here is a world where everything is on the go—from cars and spaceships to hang gliders and the imagination—forever moving Guests forward.

Spaceship Earth Attraction
This grand geosphere is almost as iconic as the Mouse himself. Inside, Dame Judi Dench narrates the sixteen-minute journey through time and space. Guests relive the history of human communication, and then delve into hands-on activities at the Project Tomorrow post show.

Innoventions

The Innoventions campus offers many interactive experiences—from becoming a fireman to inventing a roller coaster. Outside, the Fountain of Nations shoots water 150 feet high as streams dance along to timeless symphonies.

Where in the World?

Think you know where to find these Disney details? Check the inside cover to see if you're right!

a

b

39

innoventions

The Seas with Nemo & Friends Pavilion

Climb aboard, explorers! Ride in a clamshell as Nemo, Marlin, and Dory discover the wonders of their watery world at The Seas with Nemo & Friends Attraction. Then meet the real creatures of the Big Blue, chat with the laid-back sea turtle, Crush, and wander through Bruce's Shark World.

The Land Pavilion

Enjoy the sights, sounds, and smells of California while gently hang gliding aboard the Soarin' Attraction. After that, board a boat and relax while floating through the Living with the Land Attraction and learning about the latest advances in farming and gardening.

Imagination Pavilion

Creativity and laughter run rampant when a little purple dragon named Figment reminds Guests that imagination is best when unleashed. Next door, catch the Honey, I Shrunk the Audience Attraction.

41

Where in the World?

Think you know where to find these Disney details? Check the inside cover to see if you're right!

a

b

Mission: SPACE Attraction

Three . . . two . . . one . . . blast off! Train as a navigator, pilot, commander, or engineer to lead the first shuttle to Mars. With the intense sensation of the craft's g-force, experience the true-to-life rush of liftoff. Then come together as a team to successfully complete the mission.

Test Track Attraction

The Test Track Attraction *brakes* all the rules of the road as vehicles race on an exhilarating course full of dark tunnels, extreme temperatures, and surprise car maneuvers—all gearing up for a speedy sprint along an open-air track.

Universe of Energy Pavilion

What do winged pteranodons, Alex Trebek, and Albert Einstein have in common? Each is a part of Ellen DeGeneres's zany (but informative) dream during this forty-five-minute multimedia voyage. Mirrored solar panels—which give the building its outer disco-ball look—help power the vehicles inside.

a

Where in the World?

Think you know where to find these Disney details? Check the inside cover to see if you're right!

b

43

44

World Showcase Area

Think it's possible for someone to visit eleven international hot spots in one day without a having a passport, getting jet lag, or traveling by way of a time machine? You bet! Guests can roam the globe and immerse themselves in all the rich cultures offered through the World Showcase Area.

Canada Pavilion

Towering carved totems and a thirty-foot-high waterfall capture the majesty of this proud land. The CircleVision film, *O Canada!*, takes viewers through the home of the maple leaf, while the Le Cellier Steakhouse offers favorites like pretzel rolls and Canadian cheddar cheese soup.

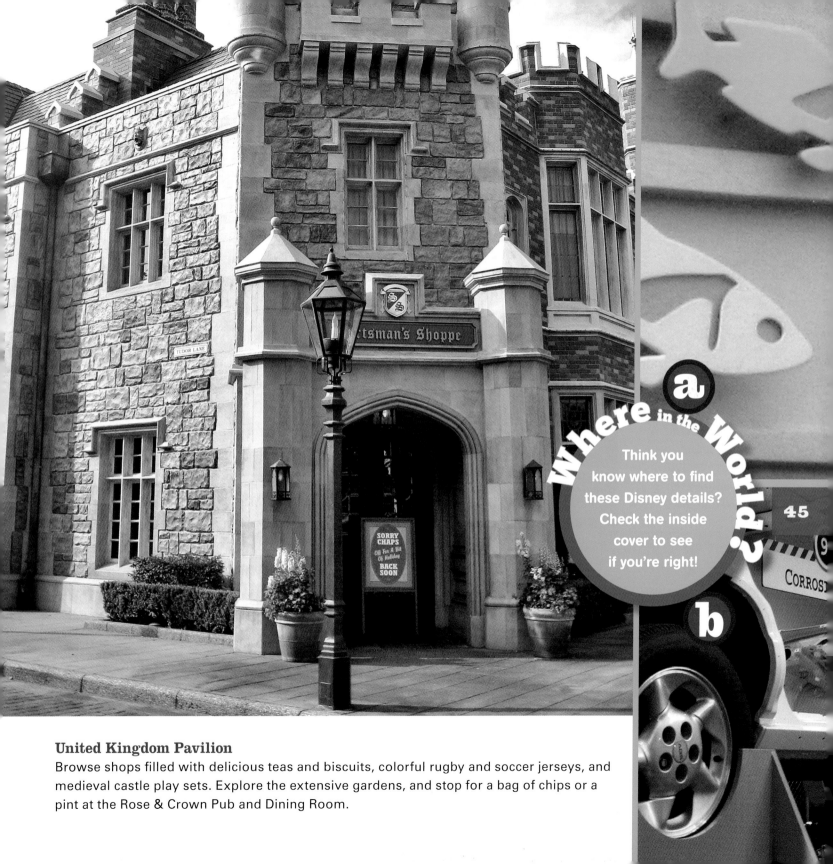

SORRY
CHAPS
Off For A Bit
Of Holiday
BACK
SOON

TUDOR LANE

...tsman's Shoppe

Where in the World?

Think you know where to find these Disney details? Check the inside cover to see if you're right!

a

b

45

9

CORROS...

United Kingdom Pavilion

Browse shops filled with delicious teas and biscuits, colorful rugby and soccer jerseys, and medieval castle play sets. Explore the extensive gardens, and stop for a bag of chips or a pint at the Rose & Crown Pub and Dining Room.

France Pavilion

Set on the banks of the main waterways of *Epcot*®, the France Pavilion, complete with its own Eiffel Tower, invites Guests to stroll through its gardens and around the fountain pool, drink wine, and listen to romantic melodies. Charming storefronts and restaurants line the streets with warm and welcoming awnings. Stop for a sweet treat at the Boulangerie Patisserie before enjoying one of the many street performances.

ⓐ Where in the World? ⓑ

Think you know where to find these Disney details? Check the inside cover to see if you're right!

Morocco Pavilion

Uniting the past with the present, the Morocco Pavilion provides Guests with an abundance of shops featuring fezzes, Rabat carpets, and woven belts. While dining on authentic Moroccan fare like chicken couscous, roasted lamb mechoui, and harira soup, belly dancers entrance diners with their beaded outfits and impressive dance moves.

47

Japan Pavilion
The sounds of the taiko-drum show captivate Guests daily at the Japan Pavilion. Koi ponds, rock gardens, and bamboo surround a larger-than-life blue pagoda filled with Japanese treasures like kimonos, samurai swords, and tea-ceremony kits. Raise your chopsticks during a high-energy hibachi show at the Teppan Edo Restaurant, or grab a quick taste at the paper-lantern-lit Yakitori House eatery.

Where in the **World?**

a

Think you know where to find these Disney details? Check the inside cover to see if you're right!

b

The American Adventure Pavilion

Outdoor kiosks full of funnel cakes, smoked turkey legs, and Samuel Adams brews entice Guests with classic food fare. Colonial American drummers and fife players perform in red-brick courtyards, while an eight-person a cappella group sings patriotic tunes inside the rotunda. This grand hall, filled with well-known paintings and quotes, provides a quick blast of American history and sets the stage for the *Audio-Animatronics* Figures show inside.

Italy Pavilion

Mangia! Partake in all the culinary pleasures of Italy. Enjoy savory pasta or antipasto dishes, while surrounded by fresco-covered walls at the Tutto Italia Ristorante, or snack on a cannoli, gelato, or coffee to go. With gondola-laden waterways, olive tree—lined storefronts, and replicas of famous Italian landmarks, the pavilion showcases the beauty, history, and charm of this picturesque country.

Germany Pavilion

Grab your lederhosen, raise your stein, and get ready to enjoy all the delights of *Deutschland*! Set among a quaint cobblestone plaza—complete with a cuckoo-clock tower and a fountain of St. George slaying a dragon—shops sell intricately crafted toys, hand-painted eggs, and crystal jewelry alongside two authentic eateries, including a bountiful bratwurst-and-more buffet with live oompah music and dancers.

Where in the World?

Think you know where to find these Disney details? Check the inside cover to see if you're right!

a

b

China Pavilion

Unwind while wandering around the peaceful gardens and reflecting pools inspired by one of the world's oldest civilizations. Sample authentic dishes like dim sum or spicy General Tso's chicken dumplings; soar over the Great Wall, the cityscapes of Beijing and Shanghai, and majestic countryside scenery during the CircleVision film *Reflections of China*; and marvel at the incredible acrobatic feats and musical talents of courtyard performers.

Where in the World?

Think you know where to find these Disney details? Check the inside cover to see if you're right!

(a)

(b)

53

Norway Pavilion

Get ready to *utforske* the land of the Vikings and Norse gods. Voyage in a longboat aboard the thrilling Maelstrom Attraction or peruse shops filled with hand-knitted sweaters, knobby trolls, and other fineries. For a tasty treat at the Kringla Bakeri Og Kafe, try sweet pretzels (*kringlas*), Norwegian school bread, and cloudberry horns, or sit down to a hearty meal fit for a princess inside the Akershus Royal Banquet Hall.

a

Think you
know where to find
these Disney details?
Check the inside
cover to see
if you're right!

54

b

Mexico Pavilion

Vamanos to the giant pyramid fashioned after an actual Aztec temple to discover a collection of historical Mexican artifacts. Alluring Latin beats resound as Guests dine on favorites like freshly made guacamole and crab-filled, fried-corn tortillas. Aboard the boat ride, float past a darkened foggy lagoon located at the bottom of a volcano and enter a fiesta of lights, colors, and music with Donald Duck and friends.

NIGHTTIME MAGIC AND IMAGINATION

IllumiNations: Reflections of Earth Nighttime Spectacular

The twelve-minute, three-act show begins with "Chaos," as fire shoots sixty feet into the air. Then the tempo mellows with "Order," as the world's first spherical video display gently glides along the World Showcase Lagoon, broadcasting images of celebrated people and events. The finale triumphantly erupts with "Meaning," as brilliant laser lights zoom and fireworks thunder against a powerful music score.

DISNEY'S HOLLYWOOD STUDIOS

NOW PLAYING "A
A CAST OF TH

BRAWNY
PAPER TOWELS

MICKEY'S

PROSPECT AVE.

GO

HOLLYWOOD
STUDIOS

Hollywood Boulevard and Starring Icons

Rewind to the glitz of 1940s Hollywood—a glamorous world filled with flashy art deco facades. Lined with curious goods and bustling with hilarious street performers brighter and bolder than movies on the silver screen, the boulevard ends with a 122-foot-high, blue-and-gold Sorcerer Mickey hat. Not viewable from this street, but just as iconic to the park is the Earffel Tower, which plays a paramount role—acting as a working water tower and supporting a five-thousand-pound pair of Mouse ears.

"SPECTACULAR JOURNEY INTO THE MOVIES" NOW PLAYING
OUSANDS! A SWEEPING SPECTACLE OF THRILLS! CHILLS! ROMANCE!

where in the World?

a

Think you
know where to find
these Disney details?
Check the inside
cover to see
if you're right!

b

The Great Movie Ride Attraction

Upon entering the Chinese Theater, Guests discover a rotating display of tinsel. Here is a town of treasures, like Dorothy Gale's ruby slippers and Mary Poppins's magical merry-go-round horse. On board the attraction vehicles, audiences reel through a celluloid chronicle of Gene Kelly singing in the rain, Sigourney Weaver dodging unwelcomed shipmates, and Harrison Ford uncovering a lost treasure in a snake-filled chamber.

58

Disney Junior—Live on Stage! Attraction

Meeska, Mooska, Mickey Mouse. No password necessary here to enjoy the twenty-two-minute live show where all Mouseketeers-at-heart watch their favorite characters step out of the television and onto the stage.

The Magic of Disney Animation Attraction

Some say a picture is worth a thousand words, so imagine the worth of the thousands upon thousands of pictures needed to make just one animated movie. Here, Disney animators present Guests with an insider's look at this process and more.

Voyage of The Little Mermaid Attraction

Don't get cold fins now! Ariel, Sebastian, and even the nasty Ursula *seas* the stage with favorites like "Part of Your World," "Under the Sea," and "Poor Unfortunate Souls." Vividly colored sea-creature puppets and live performers sway to the calypso beats like the waves lapping above the audience in this "underwater" theater.

Where in the World?

Think you know where to find these Disney details? Check the inside cover to see if you're right!

a

b

60

Walt Disney: One Man's Dream Attraction

Walt Disney once said, "Get a good idea and stay with it. Dog it, and work at it until it's done, and done right." Amid this self-guided tour through photograph-filled exhibits, Guests can see many of Walt's good ideas come to life. Watch over four hundred film clips, listen to archival interviews, and even see the second-grade desk of the man whose dreams were big enough to inspire us all.

Where in the World?

a

Think you know where to find these Disney details? Check the inside cover to see if you're right!

b

Toy Story Mania! Attraction

Step right up and try your luck! Everyone is a winner with the gang from *Toy Story* (1995). Through this next-generation dark ride, a myriad of carnival-like games challenge Guests; practice pie tossing or evading water balloons before they pop and splash. But don't worry: no one leaves cherry-stained or soaking wet. All but the fun is virtual here.

Studio Backlot Tour Attraction
Action! Hop on a two hundred-person shuttle for a behind-the-scenes pass to the movie costume, camera, props, and lighting departments. Then detour through a hot set exploding with gas-tank fires, major flooding, and earthquake-like jolts at Catastrophe Canyon.

Honey, I Shrunk the Kids Movie Set Adventure Attraction
With oversize cookies, thirty-foot-high blades of grass, and ants large enough to hold full-grown adults, the eleven-thousand-square-foot play area proves to be a colossal good time. Don't be alarmed by the forty-foot bumblebee though; it's just hanging out minding its own beeswax.

Where in the **World?**

Think you know where to find these Disney details? Check the inside cover to see if you're right!

a

b

63

Lights, Motors, Action! Extreme Stunt Show Attraction

Start your engines for the fast-paced action of twenty cars, ten motorcycles, and even a few Jet Skis rip-roaring through a gripping live show. Professional stunt drivers man the steering wheels of custom-built European cars with 150 horsepower under their hoods.

Streets of America Area

Watch out for cable cars in the city that never sleeps. In this mash-up of West Coast meets East Coast, San Francisco, California, and New York, New York, are just a block away from each other.

Muppet*Vision 3-D Attraction

Wacka-wacka: Guests need not speak fluent Muppet to understand that comedy is the special guest star in town! Kermit and the gang aim to entertain during on open-house tour of Muppet Labs, but chaos ensues when Waldo, the spirit of 3-D, flies off the screen.

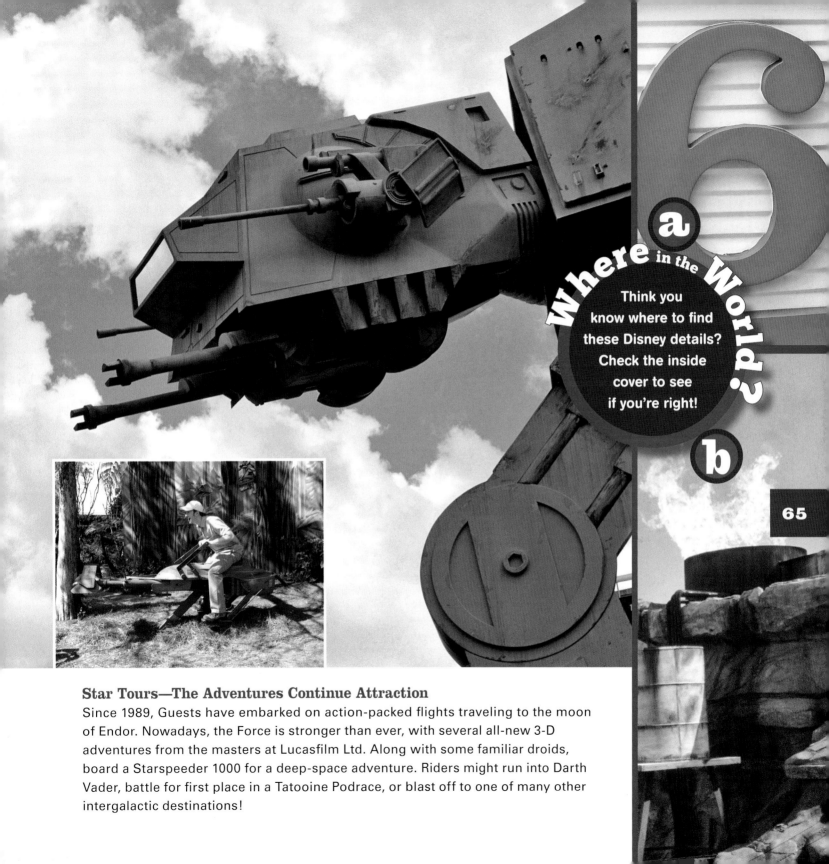

Where in the **World?**

a

Think you know where to find these Disney details? Check the inside cover to see if you're right!

b

65

Star Tours—The Adventures Continue Attraction

Since 1989, Guests have embarked on action-packed flights traveling to the moon of Endor. Nowadays, the Force is stronger than ever, with several all-new 3-D adventures from the masters at Lucasfilm Ltd. Along with some familiar droids, board a Starspeeder 1000 for a deep-space adventure. Riders might run into Darth Vader, battle for first place in a Tatooine Podrace, or blast off to one of many other intergalactic destinations!

Indiana Jones™ Epic Stunt Spectacular! Attraction

Follow the exhilarating escapades of everyone's favorite archaeologist and adventurer, Indiana Jones. This thirty-minute, on-set extravaganza is filled with dozens of stuntmen, a few incredible explosions, and, of course, one very big boulder.

Sounds Dangerous
with Drew Carey Attraction

This whodunit show, open seasonally, takes place with Guests mostly in the dark listening through state-of-the-art headphones to Drew Carey—who's armed only with his verbal wit—as he tries to solve a pesky crime.

NOW PLAYING

abc Sound Studio

SOUNDS DANGEROUS

a

Where in the World?

Think you know where to find these Disney details? Check the inside cover to see if you're right!

b

abc Sound Studio

HEAR IT........HERE NOW

The Twilight Zone Tower of Terror Attraction

Gathering dust at the end of Sunset Boulevard, the Hollywood Tower Hotel is past its prime. There, the brave-at-heart travel into the fifth dimension of sight and sound to join five unfortunate souls reliving a haunted Halloween past. Seemingly with a mind of its own, a ghoulish elevator inside free-falls and lifts until Guests feel as if up is down and down is up.

a

Where in the **World?**

Think you know where to find these Disney details? Check the inside cover to see if you're right!

b

69

Beauty and the Beast—Live on Stage Attraction

With voice-overs from the film's original cast, this stage show retells the beloved 1991 movie that also inspired a Broadway show. Guests are invited to "Be Our Guest" by fast-moving, fancy flatware ready to sing and dance. It's a Tale As Old As Time that enchants Guests of all ages.

Rock 'n' Roller Coaster Attraction

Wait a minute! I love that idea. Guests rock out as a stretch limo fighting intense California traffic weaves, bobs, and even loops upside down along 3,400 feet of roller coaster track.

Where in the World?

a

Think you know where to find these Disney details? Check the inside cover to see if you're right!

b

70

NIGHTTIME MAGIC AND IMAGINATION

Fantasmic!
Mickey Mouse's dream comes to life in an astounding fireworks display with fifty live performers and three enormous water screens projecting a cast of animated favorites—including a slew of Disney villains.

A New Species of Theme Park

Welcome! Or, *Tervetuloa! Swaagatam! Huan ying! A jarama!* Lush green fauna, sweet-smelling flowers, and fascinating animals like giant anteaters, Chinese deer, and dazzlingly colored exotic birds greet Guests to the Park. The Oasis Area is no mirage, but a peaceful haven immersing its visitors within a tropical paradise. Once crossing the bridge to the Discovery Island Area (the Park's central hub), the towering Tree of Life comes into view. With more than 325 animal images carved into a fifty-foot-wide trunk, the tree honors the perfect harmony of all the living things that call this place home.

KINGDOM THEME PARK

Where in the World?

a

Think you
know where to find
these Disney details?
Check the inside
cover to see
if you're right!

b

Discovery Island Trails Attraction

Surrounding the Tree of Life is a maze of garden pathways.
Here, investigate dark caves and cross over wooden
footbridges. Find ring-tailed lemurs bounding from branch
to branch, a Galapágos tortoise warming in the sun, and
much more.

It's Tough to be a Bug! Attraction

Burrowed at the base of the Tree of Life, Flik and company put on a 3-D exhibition to educate Guests—who are equipped with special bug-viewing glasses—about the miniature world of insects. But the disgruntled Hopper has other plans and unleashes hornets and spiders upon the audience. Can the two sides ever come together?

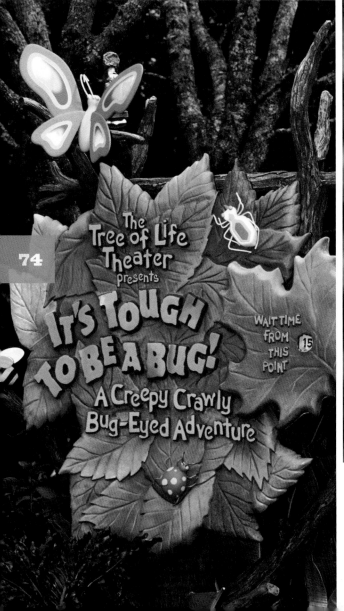

Camp Minnie-Mickey Area

Blaze a trail to have a good ol' meet and greet with some of Disney's beloved characters, like Mickey and Minnie Mouse, Rafiki, and Baloo!

Festival of The Lion King Attraction

Hosted by Timon, the thirty-minute musical revue entertains with favorites like "Can You Feel the Love Tonight" and "Circle of Life" from the 1994 movie. With powerful vocalists donning vibrant African dress and acrobats whirling above the audience in aerial ballet, it's enough to leave Guests *roaring* with applause.

Where in the **World?**

Think you know where to find these Disney details? Check the inside cover to see if you're right!

a

b

Africa Area

Travel to the land of a thousand languages. The bustling Mombasa Marketplace offers Guests the opportunity to go home with handmade treasures like woven baskets, carved wooden masks, and stone jewelry. Follow the delicious fragrance of curry and tandoori to the Tusker House Restaurant for a delectable buffet filled with different couscous dishes, baba ghanoush, and banana-cinnamon bread pudding.

76

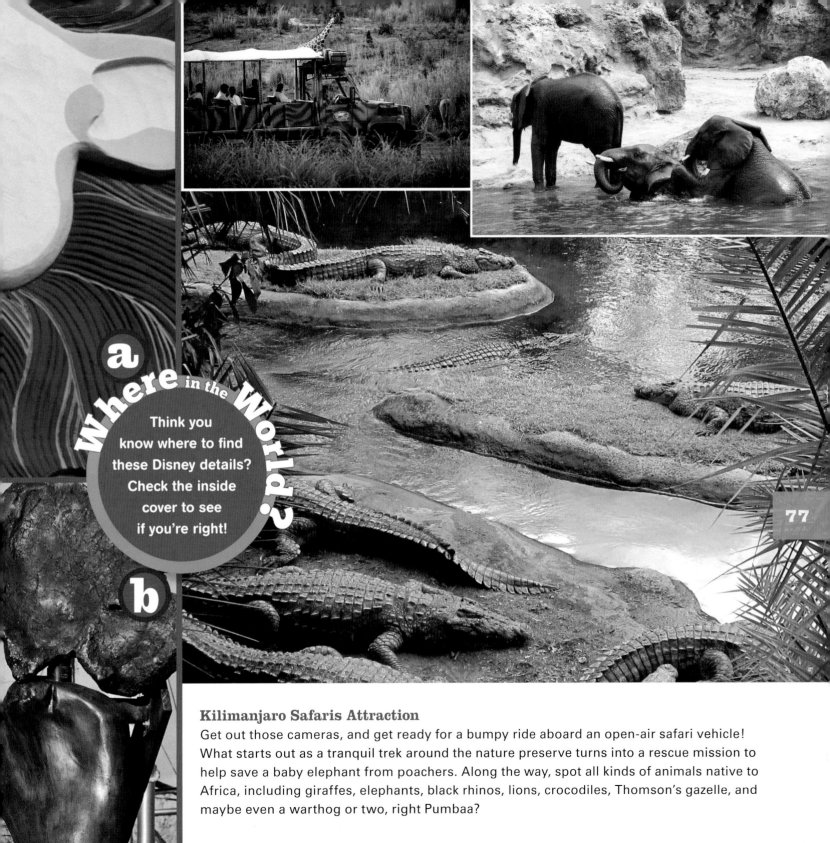

a

Where in the World?

Think you know where to find these Disney details? Check the inside cover to see if you're right!

b

Kilimanjaro Safaris Attraction

Get out those cameras, and get ready for a bumpy ride aboard an open-air safari vehicle! What starts out as a tranquil trek around the nature preserve turns into a rescue mission to help save a baby elephant from poachers. Along the way, spot all kinds of animals native to Africa, including giraffes, elephants, black rhinos, lions, crocodiles, Thomson's gazelle, and maybe even a warthog or two, right Pumbaa?

78

Pangani Forest Exploration Trail Attraction

Journey over a suspension bridge to view our distant cousins, the gorillas, who make their home in this lush forest area. Also along the trail, visit the hippos seen during the Kilimanjaro Safaris Attraction from a new angle: underwater. Even get up close with some meerkats and naked mole rats. Don't worry, they're not bashful.

Where in the **World?**

(a) (b)

Think you know where to find these Disney details? Check the inside cover to see if you're right!

79

Wildlife Express Train Attraction and Rafiki's Planet Watch Attraction

Jambo! In the village of Harambe, board a steam-powered locomotive for a five-and-a-half-minute trip past the night quarters of various animals (including elephants and rhinos) seen from the Kilimanjaro Safaris Attraction. Then arrive at the Rafiki's Planet Watch Attraction. In this indoor labyrinth of hands-on activities and demonstrations, Guests of all ages learn about the world's latest wildlife conservation efforts and how Cast Members care for the animals at *Disney's Animal Kingdom* Theme Park.

Asia Area

Bright and ornate as a tiled mosaic, the Asia Area spills over with influences from all over the world's largest continent—be it a serene temple or a dense rain forest brimming with exotic life. Explore flavors unique to Asia in delicacies such as cha siu bao, Pho, and chicken with Anandapur glaze at the Nepal-inspired Yak & Yeti Restaurant.

Flights of Wonder Attraction

Birds don't always need to be of a feather to flock together. Meet more than twenty different species of birds in this open-air theater, as some amazing feathered friends fly their way to fame.

Think you know where to find these Disney details? Check the inside cover to see if you're right!

Kali River Rapids Attraction

Get a sense of what it would be like to become an ecotourist, visiting an untouched area of the rain forest. The twelve-seater raft twists and turns atop the river, spilling cool water onto its passengers with each jostle and jolt from the fast-paced currents.

Maharajah Jungle Trek Attraction

Watch a Komodo dragon lazily climb over rocks looking for the perfect place to sun. The sounds of birds calling to each other from within their sanctuary beckon Guests along the trail, but not before curious onlookers pay a visit to some giant fruit bats. But the diamond in the rough waits farther down the path, where Asian tigers meander across ancient ruins in a temple area impressive enough to make even Shere Khan jealous.

a

Where in the **World?**

Think you know where to find these Disney details? Check the inside cover to see if you're right!

b

Expedition Everest Attraction

Join an expedition party headed for the arctic abyss of Mount Everest on this nonstop thrill ride. Board a high-speed tea train, climb to the highest peaks, and zoom through ice caverns—forward *and* backward! Just make sure to watch out for the guardian of the mountain: the infamous Yeti. He could be hiding around any corner....

The Boneyard Dig Site

Future paleontologists romp and stomp around like primeval predators at this playground, complete with prehistoric slides and a fossil-filled maze. Dig up the truth, literally, through a bone excavation and discover clues to solve the mystery of the woolly mammoth.

DinoLand U.S.A. Area

Catch the kitsch at the DinoLand U.S.A. Area, where classic fairground fun and roadside-diner delights meet the legendary giants of the past. Interactive games mix with the investigations into dinosaur bones, fossils, and even time travel—and it's all guaranteed to offer up an adventure that's sure to end with a Big Bang.

Finding Nemo— The Musical Attraction

Dive under the sea for a tuneful treat! With original songs by Tony Award— winning composer Robert Lopez and puppets designed by Michael Curry, of Broadway's *The Lion King* fame, this new musical swims into the hearts and minds of all who witness its watery wonders.

Where in the World?

a

Think you know where to find these Disney details? Check the inside cover to see if you're right!

b

Chester & Hester's Dino-Rama! Area

Amid the tempting carnival booths, the Primeval Whirl Attraction looks like a fairground roller coaster on loan from an old amusement park, but Guests best hold on during this wobbly, winding time twirl. Nearby, younger Guests can soar up amongst the trees aboard their own friendly yellow dinosaur on the TriceraTop Spin Attraction.

EST. 1947

Where in the World?

a **b**

Think you know where to find these Disney details? Check the inside cover to see if you're right!

Dinosaur Attraction

Go back in time—like sixty-five million years back—to rescue the last iguanodon from extinction. Sitting in jeep-like Time Rovers, Guests are hurled and heaved in all directions as they attempt to complete the mission. But there's danger around every turn, and time travelers are constantly reminded that everything (and everyone) is on the menu in the prehistoric world.

87

88

Downtown Disney Area

This scenic shopping, dining, and recreation area offers a treat for every taste!

Downtown Disney Marketplace Area

Shopping: Arribas Bros.; The Art of Disney; Basin; Disney Design-A-Tee; Disney's Days Of Christmas; Disney's Pin Traders; Goofy's Candy Co.; LEGO Imagination Center; Mickey's Pantry; Once Upon A Toy; Team Mickey; TrenD; World of Disney

Food and drinks: Cap'n Jack's Restaurant; Earl of Sandwich; Fulton's Crab House; Ghirardelli Soda Fountain & Chocolate Shop; Pollo Campero; Rainforest Café; T-REX: A Prehistoric Family Adventure; Wolfgang Puck Express

Activities: Marina & Boat Rental; Disney Magic Music Days concert pavilion

Hyperion Wharf Area

Shopping: Curl by Sammy Duvall; Orlando Harley-Davidson

Food and drinks: Cookes of Dublin; Fuego by Sosa Cigars; Paradiso 37; Portobello; Raglan Irish Pub & Restaurant

Activities: New areas to come!

Where in the World?

89

Think you know where to find these Disney details? Check the inside cover to see if you're right!

a

b

Downtown Disney West Side Area

Shopping: Disney's Candy Cauldron; D-Street; Hoypoloi; Little Missmatched; Magic Masters; Magnetron Magnetz; Mickey's Groove; PoP Gallery; Sosa Family Cigars; Sunglass Icon

Food and drinks: Bongos Cuban Café; House of Blues; Planet Hollywood; Wolfgang Puck Café; Wetzels Pretzels

Activities: "Characters in Flight" hot-air balloon; *Cirque du Soleil*: La Nouba; *DisneyQuest* Indoor Interactive Theme Park; AMC 24 Theatres

Disney's Typhoon Lagoon Water Park

Humunga Kowabunga, dude! That's the name of the trio of speed slides sending Guests down five stories in seconds—and the thrills don't stop there! Within this tropical paradise, topsy-turvy water coasters, waterfall-laden body slides, and a shark-populated snorkeling lagoon make Guests grateful for some slow-down time, including beach lounging by the Surf Pool or lazily drifting along the more than two-thousand-foot waterway encircling the Park.

Disney's Blizzard Beach Water Park
With the appearance of a snow-covered ski sanctuary, this park is one of the best ways to stay cool on a warm, sunny Florida day. Atop Mount Gushmore, the 360-foot Summit Plummet flume offers a "chilling" plunge. The rushes keep coming with a double-hump slide, a triplet of flumes, and even an eight-lane Toboggan Racers waterslide!

a

where in the World?

b

Think you know where to find these Disney details? Check the inside cover to see if you're right!

Golfing

Four, 18-hole golf courses have become stops along the PGA Tour and entice Guests for a day of driving and putting. Just across from Disney's Polynesian Resort, the Palm & Magnolia Golf Studio offers lessons in addition to the classic courses. Nestled in nearby woodlands is the Disney's Osprey Ridge Golf Course, while the treelined Disney's Lake Buena Vista Golf Course is framed by Disney's Saratoga Springs Resort & Spa and Disney's Old Key West Resort. For something more whimsical, the Disney's Fantasia Gardens Miniature Golf Course challenges Guests with musical xylophone stairs and dancing-hippo intrusions, and Christmas carols play year-round at Santa's vacation retreat, Disney's Winter Summerland Miniature Golf Course.

ESPN Wide World of Sports Complex

Whether watching an Atlanta Braves baseball game during spring training, participating in an amateur-league volleyball match, or taking to the tennis courts, Guests get their game on at this 220-acre facility hosting more than thirty types of sports.

93

Where in the World?

Think you know where to find these Disney details? Check the inside cover to see if you're right!

a

b

Resorts

Waterways play a huge role within the *Walt Disney World* Resort. The Seven Seas Lagoon and Bay Lake bring the resorts around the *Magic Kingdom* Park together. Here, Guests can hop from the South Seas and the Pacific Northwest to a Victorian beach retreat, a picturesque campground, and the hotel of the future. For the resorts by *Epcot*®, connection is all about friendship—with a series of *FriendShip* passenger boats transporting Guests along Crescent Lake and its canals. Linking to the Downtown Disney Area are channels from resorts themed to Key West, New Orleans, and upstate, New York, though that's not to shortchange landlocked resorts like the ones inspired by African safaris or larger-than-life objects. As with all the resorts, these hot spots are connected to the rest of the World through an impressive bus network.

PIONEER HALL

HERE TONIGHT
THE
HOOP-DEE-DOO
REVUE

SEATING TIMES 5:00 P.M. 7:15 P.M. & 9:30 P.M.

MENU

ALL YOU CAN EAT HOME-STYLE VITTLES
CHOW DOWN ON...
BUCKETS OF FRIED CHICKEN AND SMOKED PORK RIBS
BEST IN THE WILDERNESS!
PLENTY OF SIDE FIXIN'S AND MA'S FAMOUS DESSERT
WET YOUR WHISTLES WITH BEER, WINE, AND SODAS

INCLUDES SHOW, DINNER AND BEVERAGE
SALES TAX AND GRATUITY INCLUDED IN PRICE
FOR RESERVATIONS, PLEASE CALL 939-3463

Where in the World?

a

b

Think you
know where to find
these Disney details?
Check the inside
cover to see
if you're right!

Photography by **BECKIE EASTWOOD** on pages 89 (door entrance), 95b; **DEBORAH EASTWOOD** on front cover (Disney's Hollywood Studios), back cover (topiary), and pages 3b, 9a, 11 (interior and exterior), 12 (all images), 14 (attraction), 15b, 16 (raft), 17 (group), 21 (topiary), 22 (characters), 23 (FASTPASS Service sign), 30 (all images), 32 (Space Mountain Attraction), 34 (aliens), 35 (sign), 36, 39a, 43a, 43b, 46 (posters), 53a, 53b, 53 (exterior), 54a, 56 (all images), 57b, 59a, 65a, 67a, 67b, 70a, 76, 77 (elephants and crocodiles), 83b, 83 (mountain peak with flags), 88 (statue in the water), 93a, 93b, 94 (Grand Floridian Resort & Spa), 95 (menu); **JENNIFER EASTWOOD** on front cover (close-ups of the Spaceship Earth Attraction and the clock) and pages 4 (cart), 5a, 7a, 7b, 8 (tiki), 9b, 11b, 13a, 13b,

14 (building exterior), 15a, 15 (train), 17b, 18 (all images), 21b, 21 (boat), 23a, 25a, 25b, 27a, 27b, 29b, 31a, 32 (Astro Orbiter Attraction), 33a, 33b, 35a, 35b, 37a, 38 (Future World Area landscape and close-up of the Spaceship Earth Attraction), 41b, 41 (exterior), 42 (Mission: SPACE Attraction sign), 44 (lagoon), 45 (all images), 47b, 47 (exterior and fezzes), 49a, 51a, 51b, 52 (all images), 54b, 54 (skeletons), 57 (marquee), 62 (ant), 65 (speeder bike), 67 (studio signs), 73 (flowers), 79a; **CHRISTINA GAUDRAULT** on pages 9 (tree), 10 (rhinos and gorillas), 16 (train), 34 (interior), 31a; **ALFRED GIULIANI** on back cover (horse and statue) and pages 7 (statue), 19 (mansion exterior), 19b, 24 (all images), 25 (daytime and icicle exteriors), 26 (Donald Duck), 49b, 50 (gondolas), 75 (giraffe); **JASON WOJTOWICZ** on pages 5b, 25 (night shot), 46 (sunset), 47b, 53 (troll), 63a, 68 (exterior), 78 (gorilla); and **GREG WHEELER** on pages 59b, 73b, 75b, 80 (signs), 82 (bat), 85a, 91a.

All rights reserved. Published by Disney Editions, an imprint of Disney Book Group. No part of this book may be reproduced or transmitted in any form or by any means, electronic or mechanical, including photocopying, recording, or by any information storage and retrieval system, without written permission from the publisher.

For information address Disney Editions, 114 Fifth Avenue, New York, New York 10011-5690.
Editorial Director: Wendy Lefkon
Associate Editor: Jessica Ward
Designed by Jon Glick

Printed in Singapore
First Edition
10 9 8 7 6 5 4 3 2 1
ISBN 978-1-4231-4456-4
F850-6835-5-11196

D23
The Official Disney Fan Club

Disney.com/D23